READING CORNER

PHONICS

Sniff Gets Digging

Written by
Clare De Marco

Illustrated by
James Cottell

Practising CVCC and
CCVC plus polysyllabic words

First published in 2010 by
Franklin Watts
338 Euston Road
London NW1 3BH

Franklin Watts Australia
Hachette Children's Books
Level 17/207 Kent Street
Sydney NSW 2000

Text © Clare De Marco 2010
Illustration © James Cottell 2010

A CIP catalogue record for this book
is available from the British Library.

ISBN: 978 0 7496 9166 0 (hbk)
ISBN: 978 0 7496 9175 2 (pbk)

Series Editor: Jackie Hamley
Series Advisors: Dr Barrie Wade,
 Dr Hilary Minns
Series Designer: Jonathan Hair

Printed in China

Franklin Watts is a division of
Hachette Children's Books,
an Hachette UK company
www.hachette.co.uk

There is a puzzle at the end of this book.
Here are the answers for you to check later!

The matching words are:

Sniff cliff, stiff

crab drab, slab

stick brick, click, flick, trick

swing bring, fling, sling, sting

"Let's go out with Sniff," said Alex.

"Yes!" said Jen.

"Have a sandwich for a snack," said Gran.

5

Sniff and the children
went to the swings.

Sniff dug in the sand.

"What can Sniff smell?" said Alex.

"Is it a stick?" said Jen.

Sniff kept digging in the sand.

13

"It's not a stick," said Alex.
"Yuck! My sandwich is
full of sand!"

"I think it's a log," said Jen.

"Stop it, Sniff!"

But Sniff kept on digging.

"Come out of there and go for a swim, Sniff," said Alex. "Get rid of all that sand!"

But Sniff still kept on digging.

"Has Sniff got it yet?" said Jen.

Then there was a little yelp.

"I think IT has got Sniff!"
said Alex.

"It's a crab!" said Jen.

"Back you go, crab!" said Alex.

"And no digging, Sniff!" said Jen.

Puzzle Time!

Match the words that rhyme
to the pictures.

Sniff

cliff

fling

brick

slab

crab

flick

trick

stick

drab

click

bring

sling

swing

stiff

sting

See page 2 for answers.

Notes for parents and teachers

READING CORNER PHONICS has been structured to provide maximum support for children learning to read through synthetic phonics. The stories are designed for independent reading but may also be used by adults for sharing with young children.

The teaching of early reading through synthetic phonics focuses on the 44 sounds in the English language, and how these sounds correspond to their written form in the 26 letters of the alphabet. Carefully controlled vocabulary makes these books accessible for children at different stages of phonics teaching, progressing from simple CVC (consonant-vowel-consonant) words such as "top" (t-o-p) to trisyllabic words such as "messenger" (mess-en-ger). READING CORNER PHONICS allows children to read words in context, and also provides visual clues and repetition to further support their reading. These books will help develop the all important confidence in the new reader, and encourage a love of reading that will last a lifetime!

If you are reading this book with a child, here are a few tips:

1. Talk about the story before you start reading. Look at the cover and the title. What might the story be about? Why might the child like it?

2. Encourage the child to reread the story, and to retell the story in their own words, using the illustrations to remind them what has happened.

3. Discuss the story and see if the child can relate it to their own experience, or perhaps compare it to another story they know.

4. Give praise! Small mistakes need not always be corrected. If a child is stuck on a word, ask them to try and sound it out and then blend it together again, or model this yourself. For example "wish" w-i-sh "wish".

READING CORNER PHONICS covers two grades of synthetic phonics teaching, with three levels at each grade. Each level has a certain number of words per story, indicated by the number of bars on the spine of the book:

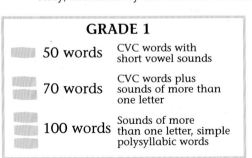

GRADE 1

50 words	CVC words with short vowel sounds
70 words	CVC words plus sounds of more than one letter
100 words	Sounds of more than one letter, simple polysyllabic words

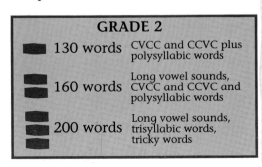

GRADE 2

130 words	CVCC and CCVC plus polysyllabic words
160 words	Long vowel sounds, CVCC and CCVC and polysyllabic words
200 words	Long vowel sounds, trisyllabic words, tricky words